# DIVERS

First published in Great Britain in 1993 by
Colin Baxter Photography Ltd
Grantown-on-Spey
Morayshire, PH26 3NA
Scotland

**British Library Cataloguing in Publication Data**
Dennis, Roy
Divers
I. Title
598.29

ISBN 0–948661–37–2

Map by Iain Sarjeant

Photography Copyright © 1993 by

Front Cover © Janos Jurka
Back Cover © Michael S Quinton
Page 1 © Laurie Campbell
Page 4 © Michael S Quinton
Page 6 © Bill Ivy
Page 8 © E K Thompson (Aquila)
Page 9 © Colin Baxter
Page 10 Top © Hannu Hautala (FLPA)
Page 10 Bottom © Janos Jurka
Page 11 © Tom Walker
Page 13 © Michael S Quinton
Page 14 © Daniel J Cox
Page 15 Top Left © Alan Williams (NHPA)
Page 15 Top Right © Dennis Bright (Swift)
Page 15 Bottom Left © Roger Tidman (NHPA)
Page 15 Bottom Right © Alan Williams (NHPA)
Page 17 © Janos Jurka
Page 18 © Michael S Quinton
Page 21 © Michael S Quinton
Page 22 Top © Michael S Quinton
Page 22 Bottom © Wayne Lankinen
Page 25 © Michael S Quinton
Page 26 © Colin Baxter
Page 27 © Michael S Quinton
Page 28 © Janos Jurka

Page 31 © Janos Jurka
Page 33 © Steven C Kaufman (Bruce Coleman)
Page 35 © Janos Jurka (Bruce Coleman)
Page 36 Top © Janos Jurka
Page 36 Bottom © Janos Jurka
Page 37 © Janos Jurka
Page 38 © Dennis Green (Bruce Coleman)
Page 41 Top © Roy Dennis
Page 41 Bottom © Hannu Hautala (FLPA)
Page 42 © Hannu Hautala (FLPA)
Page 45 © E K Thompson (Aquila)
Page 46 © Bob & Clara Calmoun (Bruce Coleman)
Page 49 © Tom Walker
Page 50 © Jen & Des Barnett (Bruce Coleman)
Page 51 © Jan Van De Kam (Bruce Coleman)
Page 52 © Tom Walker
Page 55 © Roy Dennis
Page 57 © Tom Walker
Page 58 © Tom Walker
Page 61 © Colin Baxter
Page 63 © Janos Jurka
Page 64 © Michael S Quinton
Page 67 © Roy Dennis
Page 69 © Michael S Quinton

Printed in Singapore

# DIVERS

Roy Dennis

Colin Baxter Photography, Grantown-on-Spey, Scotland

# Contents

# Divers

Wild and beautiful parts of the world are often made the more memorable by living creatures which give the place spirit. Maybe it's the breaching of great whales or the fishing plunge of an Osprey, the howl of polar wolves or the hauntingly beautiful music of Great Northern Divers. Many people have remarked on the calling of divers (loons in America) and the sensations it produces in humans; long ago John Burroughs, the celebrated American naturalist wrote:

> Some birds represent the majesty of nature, like the eagles;
>
> others its sweetness and melody, like song birds.
>
> The small loon represents its wildness and solitariness.

It's over 30 years now since I heard my first Great Northern Diver calling on the tiny island of Lundy off south-west England. Several days of fierce October storms had abated and the seas in the bay below the village were at last calm as we climbed the cliff path back home at dusk. Without warning the ghostly laughter of a newly arrived Great Northern Diver echoed upwards from the bay. It was magical, made more so by the fact that I could not see the bird on the grey ocean below. I have never lost the thrill for diver music.

In the summer of 1992, I was privileged to be introduced to Great Northern Divers on their breeding lakes in the Adirondack mountains in New York State. Looking out from Judy and Pat McIntyre's cabin, a pair of Loons moved across the still lake before me and suddenly, just before we departed, they started to duet in the evening sunlight and my memory shot back to that evening long ago at Lundy. These particular Great Northern Divers, along with many others in the northern United States, have been intensively researched and more has been learnt in the last three decades than in the previous million years. Yet divers existed then and summer nights would have brought the same threats from predators, such as raccoons or mink, as well as time to echo their territorial calls down the still waters of the lake and through the primeval forest.

In Scotland, the lochs are home to the most southerly Black-throated Divers in the world; they also make beautiful music and live in wild places. I remember one sighting as I surveyed Golden Eagles in the mountains of Sutherland, a wild and desolate landscape where the grey rocks rose from the earth's crust over 2,000 million years ago. As I climbed across the wall of the corrie towards the eagle's eyrie, the sun was rising over the tundra-

*Black-throated Diver*

like peatlands of the Flow Country stretching away to the north-east. The absolute quiet of the summer dawn was broken by the wild cackling clamour of a pair of Black-throated Divers circling down to break the still surface of a loch far below. I sat and watched as they displayed together before they quietly slipped below the gloomy waters to hunt for trout.

Nowadays I live in one of the remnants of the ancient Caledonian Forest of Scotland and in recent years a pair of Red-throated Divers has started to nest in a tiny lochan on the heathery moorland foothills of the Cairngorm mountains. It's 30 miles to the Moray Firth and the birds regularly fly there to catch salt water fish for their young. Sometimes as they pass over our farm, so high that they seem invisible, I hear their goose-like calls. This ga-ga-gag call is highly evocative and I can never hear it without thinking of the Shetland Islands where I once lived. There, the call gives the bird its name of rain goose; a portender of rain. I heard the same call this summer as I sat with friends on a large rock on one of the most northerly headlands in Spitzbergen. Half a mile ahead of us, a female polar bear and her two well-grown cubs ambled across the barren tundra disturbing a few small groups of grazing reindeer. A day later I saw another pair of divers swimming on a half thawed pond

*A Red-throated Diver sits on its nest among willow bushes*
*on a lake in Iceland. This species has a circumpolar*
*distribution with some pairs nesting only*
*500 miles from the North Pole.*

Divers are strong fliers and some birds fly many
miles to catch fish for their young.

with a herd of lumbering walrus as near neighbours. How they manage to lay eggs and rear young in such a short summer, even with the advantage of the midnight sun, I cannot imagine but the Red-throated Diver is a hardy survivor; as adapted to life in the high Arctic as to the hill lochans near my home, nearly 2,000 miles to the south.

Divers have been revered by man since time immemorial, a respect mostly inspired by their haunting calls. A multitude of legends and beliefs are associated with the native peoples of the northern world. In Siberia, Scandinavia and North America, it was believed that divers could guide the soul of the dead to a new world. The old Stone Age Innuits in Alaska even buried a diver's skull with carved ivory eyes in their graves. This link with the supernatural meant that in many lands the bird was unmolested and treated as special; however in others it was regarded as good eating with the skin and feathers used for clothing and decoration.

*White-billed Diver*

Their haunting calls and mysterious ability to disappear under the water also created many legends, while the ancient Indian tribes of North America knew many stories associated with diver music. Often they involved a person calling for a lost friend or loved one, or the echoing calls evoked the memory of a past tragedy or event. Divers were also believed to be able to restore sight by carrying a blind person to the bottom of a lake time after time until vision was restored. One legend recalls how the white necklace on the diver's back is actually a necklace of white shells given by the grateful recipient of restored eyesight. Even more magical properties are attributed to the diver in Siberia and North America where native peoples believed that at the beginning of creation the diver dived to the bottom of the sea and brought up mud on its foot for the Great Spirit or God to make the earth.

As with many wild creatures, industrial man lost his respect for divers, and the early Europeans arriving in North America shot them for food though they didn't regard the meat highly. Later it was considered good sport and a great challenge for the man with a gun because of its wary nature and great ability to escape by diving. This century it was deemed a nuisance and a competitor to man for fish and was destroyed; even I can remember fishermen in the Scottish Highlands shaking the eggs of Black-throated Divers to prevent them from hatching because they might eat too many fish.

Then like so many things in life, the wheel turns full circle and the diver is loved again by many people as a symbol of wild places and free spirits and of the need to protect and cherish our natural world. The diver has become an indicator of the damaging effects of many of today's environmental problems such as oil pollution clogging up its plumage, monafilament fishing nets drowning it at sea and a weird soup of pesticides, chemicals and acid rain harming its health and destroying its food supplies.

Divers have been around for a very long time and the earliest fossil evidence dates back 40 to 50 million years ago when the first ancestors of our present day divers lived in the Eocene epoch. The earliest diver discovered so far lived in England in the late Eocene epoch and has been given the name *anglicus*; fossil records of other species have been named from various parts of the world including France, Italy, Czechoslovakia and North America. Our present day divers evolved about 10 million years ago and nowadays five species are grouped together in the order *Gaviiformes*, the family *Gavidae* and the genus *Gavia*. All these names derive from the Latin word for a gull, a name given to it by Forster. Previously the generic name was *Colymbus*, from the German word *kolymbis* meaning a diving bird.

In English they were named after their ability in water and are called divers. The word

*A family of Great Northern Divers.*

*Pacific Divers resting on a lake in the Canadian Rockies. After breeding, divers migrate over land and along the coasts to their wintering places, where they moult into the black, grey and white winter plumage.*

*Great Northern Diver*
*White-billed Diver*

*Black-throated Diver*
*Red-throated Diver*

Loon is used in North America and is generally accepted to be of Scandinavian origin, meaning clumsy – a reference to its awkward appearance on land. Common Loons or Great Northern Divers are found principally in the United States and Canada with smaller numbers breeding in Greenland and Iceland (see distribution maps, page 70). The scientific name is *Gavia immer*. The species name is derived from the Latin word for immerse, referring to the bird's habit of disappearing under water. It is the largest of the family with the exception of the closely related White-billed Diver, *Gavia adamsii*. This species nests in the Arctic from the north of Hudson Bay westwards to the northern tundra of Alaska and on westwards across the top of Siberia to the Arctic islands of European Russia. Its scientific name commemorates Edward Adams and was given it by the biologist Asa Gray.

The Black-throated Diver *Gavia arctica*, after the Arctic, breeds in Europe and Asia, extending from Scotland in the west, across the boreal and tundra zones of Scandinavia and Russia to the Pacific coast. In Siberia, the eastern populations are slightly larger and the black throat has a green iridescence. These birds are regarded as a distinct race or subspecies of the Black-throated Diver *Gavia arctica viridigularis*, meaning green-throated. Until recently Black-throated Divers in North America (Arctic Loons) were regarded as the same species as our birds but they are now treated as a separate species. The Pacific Loon, *Gavia pacifica*, named after the Pacific Ocean, breeds from Hudson Bay westwards to Alaska, generally between latitude 60 degrees north and the Arctic Ocean, with their winter quarters along the Pacific coast of North America. In Alaska and the adjacent area of eastern Siberia there is some overlap, with Black-throated Divers reported in Alaska and Pacific Loons in Siberia. They appear to be separated ecologically with the Pacific Loon occurring farther north. Finally, the Red-throated Diver *Gavia stellata* is the most distinctively different of all five species. It lives throughout the Arctic regions of Europe, Siberia and North America. Its specific name is from the Latin for stars, referring to the white spots on the bird's back in winter.

# Great Northern Diver

The Great Northern Diver is a large bird, specially adapted to an aquatic life, with a dense waterproof plumage immaculately patterned in black and white. The upperparts are black with a green and purple gloss, the neck is adorned with vertical white stripes forming an incomplete collar and throat band, and the back is chequered with white blotches. The heavy black bill is dagger shaped while the legs and webbed feet are grey-black and the eye is red. In winter, they are rather non-descript being dark grey-brown above and white below with a white throat.

Great Northern Divers are usually observed swimming low in the water, with the bill of this species held level from the pronounced forehead in comparison to the more sloping profile of the smaller Black-throated Diver. The legs are set well back on the body so the bird is ungainly on land and rarely comes ashore except when nesting. They fly well on rather small pointed wings, although the take-off from water is laboured and the landing is just a belly flop. Underwater they are in their element and their speed and agility allow them to catch fish in full pursuit. They can dive to depths of 70 metres and remain submerged for several minutes, although their normal dive time is about 40 seconds. In freshwater they catch a wide variety of fish species but in winter while living on the coast their diet is more varied and includes crustaceans as well as fish.

The Great Northern Diver has only been proved to nest in the British Isles on one occasion and that was in Wester Ross in 1970. A hybrid Great Northern × Black-throated Diver has bred with a Black-throated Diver on the same loch in subsequent years and more recently a mixed pair of Great Northern and Black-throated Divers has also bred. Several hundred pairs nest in Iceland and others breed in Greenland, mostly on the west coast. A tiny population of one or two pairs has been recorded on Bear Island in Svalbard. The Iceland population, some of the Greenland birds and possibly even some of the Canadian Arctic birds migrate south-eastwards to winter around the Scottish coast where they are often found in small numbers in most bays from October to April. Lesser numbers occur along the coasts of Ireland, England and Wales, with stragglers occurring on inland lakes and reservoirs. Reasonable numbers also reach the mainland coasts of northern Europe.

Most of the Great Northern Divers in the world are found breeding in North America; the bulk of the population nests in Canada where it is found on lakes across the whole country with the exception of the southern parts of Saskatchewan and Alberta and the high Arctic. In the United States, it nests from Massachusetts north to Maine and west through the northern states to Idaho and Washington. For most people in North America, the Loon refers to the Great Northern Diver and it is now a well-known bird in the northern states where its image adorns car stickers, clothing and hotel signs. The main populations (approximate numbers of adults) are in Maine (3,500), New York State (800), Wisconsin (2,200) and Minnesota (10,000), but these numbers are small compared with the suggested Canadian and Alaskan population of over half a million adults. In winter, they can be found in coastal waters of the Pacific from Alaska to California and from Newfoundland down the Atlantic coast to Florida and westwards to north Mexico.

In spring, Great Northerns, resplendent in their breeding plumage, return to the breeding grounds as soon as the lakes become ice free. Males tend to arrive in late March or early April in the southern areas and are quickly joined by the females. Farther north in Canada and Alaska pairs may be at least a month later in reclaiming their territories. This is the time when their calling heralds the coming spring, a sound so beautiful and haunting that it seems to take one back to the beginning of time. Great Northern Divers nest generally on large lakes, with a minimum size of five hectares. On larger lakes pairs divide the water into separate territories and some lakes can hold many pairs, each with their own favourite haunts.

They are highly aggressive in the defence of their territories and they let other divers know of their ownership through a wonderful variety of wails, yodels and tremulo calls. On

*Divers find it difficult to walk on land, but like all other divers during courtship, this pair of Great Northern Divers have come ashore to mate in the spring.*

*Within days of hatching the young divers are able to travel on the backs of their parents.*

large lakes pairs call to each other and on still nights their music echoes through the forests and lakes of the north. Adults are generally long lived, the oldest may reach 30 years, and each spring the same pair usually returns to their own territory. Soon after arrival, they renew their partnership with gentle courtship involving close swimming, bill dipping, head shaking and mewing calls. Mating takes place on land and a nest site is chosen close to the water's edge. Often traditional nest sites are re-used from year to year and generally these are found on islands and less often on headlands. The route to the water should allow the bird to get rapidly into water deep enough for diving. Great Northern Divers can shuffle a few metres up the bank but prefer to nest close to the water. Sometimes the nest is just a scrape in the ground but at other times they gather vegetation to make substantial nests, especially in times of rising water levels.

Eggs are laid from late May, usually two days apart and the normal clutch is two, although sometimes one, but very rarely three. The eggs are large, slightly glossy olive-brown marked with dark brown spots and blotches. They weigh about 150 grams, with first eggs slightly heavier; the shape is elongated and oval. Both sexes incubate from the first egg and except when disturbed one adult is always on the nest. The incubation period is about a month and there may be a day between the hatching of the two eggs. If eggs are plundered or lost, the pair usually lay another clutch within two weeks.

The tiny chicks are covered in black down except for a white belly and within a day of hatching are led by the parents to a sheltered area of the lake which is used as a nursery bay. Here they are fed on small fish and protected from wind and waves; sometimes they ride on their parent's back. At about two weeks of age the black down is replaced by grey down and the growing young divers start to venture into more of the lake. Sometimes both adults may hunt for food but at other times, especially when the chicks are small, one adult guards the young. Adults actively defend their young from potential predators, both from aerial attacks by birds and from underwater predation by turtles and large fish. Juvenile plumage, grey above and white below, starts to appear at a month and feathering is complete between two and three months, by which time the young divers are able to fly and are catching all their own food.

Families of Great Northerns stay together through the summer but as the July days shorten, adults, especially birds which have failed to rear young, gather in groups on larger lakes. Sometimes numbers swell as single adults from families visit these social gatherings before returning to their territories. By September, the first adults are starting their autumn migration to the coasts. In North America, migration is on a broad front to both coasts as well as to the Great Lakes where large numbers congregate; many continue southwards to the warm waters of the Gulf, the Florida coast and southern California. Those nesting in Iceland and Greenland have exposed migration routes as they head over the Atlantic Ocean to the coasts of Scotland and northern Europe. Once they have reached their wintering grounds the adults commence their autumn moult and change their plumage into a grey-brown and white plumage similar to the juveniles.

Juvenile divers migrate later in the autumn and some may not move south until the lakes start to freeze in November; then like their parents they move to coastal waters. In mild winters quite large numbers of divers may stay on into the middle of winter on inland lakes and reservoirs. At sea, Great Northern Divers feed in small groups and spread out during the day, moving at dusk to deeper water where they gather in roosting groups through the night. The adults start to moult again in January, and during this time the birds are flightless for about a month as they grow new wing and tail feathers. Soon their beautiful nuptial plumage is complete and they are ready to return to their breeding territories. Now there is an urgency to return to their still chilly northern home. They gather in groups or flocks prior to departure in favourite sea-lochs and bays. Sometimes I've watched them indulging in synchronised group fishing in the sea-lochs of northern Scotland and a spring visit to Loch Eriboll is always enriched by Great Northerns in their superb summer plumage. Suddenly the young are left on their own and even in Scotland small numbers of immatures are found on the sea during their first summer of life.

*A Great Northern Diver at his most impressive.*

*Throughout the north, divers have to wait for the lakes to thaw before
breeding and often congregate on larger lakes or even open
leads of water in the Arctic Ocean. Some Great Northern
Divers even nest near areas of permanent snow fields
such as this bird living on a lake in northern Iceland.*

# Red-Throated Diver

The Red-throated Diver is a familiar bird in Scotland with its breeding grounds in the Highlands and Islands. It is the smallest of the divers and has many differences from the four other species. The Red-throated Diver gets its name from the distinctive vinaceous-red colour of the throat in breeding plumage, although the throat can look dark or even black at a distance. The head and sides of the neck are grey, streaked with white on the back of neck, extending to white stripes on the sides of the breast. The back is dark grey-brown and unmarked, unlike the other species, while the rest of the underparts are white shading to grey on the flanks. The bill is fine for a diver, upcurved and pale grey, the legs and feet are grey and black while the eye is wine-red. In winter, it's a grey bird, the pale back speckled with white and the underparts silvery white.

Red-throated Divers are strong flyers able to rise easily onto the wing; they fly high and fast with rapidly beating wings. The body is hunched in flight with head and neck bowed downwards. Descents are rapid and the diver lands belly first with a noisy splash. On the water they can swim high in a jaunty manner or nearly submerged, but the slender upturned bill is always held upwards at a distinctive angle which allows easy identification of this species. Like all divers, it is expert underwater where it catches all its prey, principally fish such as young herring, sprats and sand-eels. It can remain underwater for up to 90 seconds and often swims looking underwater before diving. On its breeding grounds, the Red-throated Diver often flies to larger lakes or even as far as the sea to catch fish for its young, which it carries back in its bill.

The Red-throated Diver is found as a breeding bird throughout the north of Scotland where it breeds mainly on moorland lochs and lochans; the strongholds are in the Highlands, the Western Isles, Orkney and Shetland, with smaller numbers south to southern Argyll. The population is believed to be between 1,200 and 1,500 pairs with about half of them breeding in Shetland. In winter numbers around the British coast are swollen by birds from Iceland, Greenland and northern Europe; favourite areas are the Moray Firth and the Aberdeenshire coast where over a thousand birds may occur. The total British population in winter is over 10,000 birds.

This species has a circumpolar distribution, north of about 60 degrees north, with breeding birds occurring throughout Russia from the Pacific Ocean to Europe, where population estimates include 2,000 pairs in Finland and 1,000 pairs in both Iceland and Norway. It is a very hardy species with birds nesting to 83 degrees north, only 500 miles from the North Pole. Siberian birds tend to be larger and those in Svalbard and Franz Joseph Land are paler. Red-throated Divers also nest in the tundra areas of Canada and Alaska, southwards in coastal districts to Labrador in the east and British Columbia in the west. In winter, they occur in coastal waters south of the breeding grounds; northern European birds winter on the coasts of the British Isles, southern Iceland and mainland Europe as well as inland on the Black and Caspian Seas and occasionally in the northern Mediterranean. Siberian birds move south to winter along the coasts of Japan and China, while North American birds winter southwards to Florida in the east and to Mexico in the west.

Red-throated Divers commence their spring migration in March soon after they moult their breeding plumage. In the southernmost nesting areas, such as in Scotland, where waters are generally ice free in March, the first pairs arrive on the nesting grounds in late March. But it may be two months later before the most northerly pairs can return to their nesting sites high above the Arctic Circle. They

Red-throated Divers have the most beautiful and intricate territorial
behaviour and displays of any of the divers; these include side-by-side
swimming, which can lead to the 'snake-dance' and the
'plesiosaur race', where the body is raised vertically in
the water and there is much excitement.

are very adaptable birds, at ease in water and in the air, so they have been able to colonise much of the land north of the tree line in the northern hemisphere and are in fact one of the most northerly breeding species in the world. They are at home on very small lakes, down to the size of a small pond just ten metres across, as well as nesting on large lakes and slow moving rivers. Nesting sites are generally in tundra and moorland or mountainous country, from sea level to 700 metres in altitude, but also in clearings and lakes in the northern boreal forest. Often the nesting site contains little or no food and the birds must fly to the sea or larger lakes to fish. In consequence, populations are higher in coastal areas. Generally they are solitary nesters but on large lakes they may be partly colonial.

Red-throated Divers have the most elaborate of displays of all the divers as well as a haunting repertoire of wails, screams, cackles, growls and moaning calls. In flight, the call is a distinctive goose-like call, 'ga-ga-gag' of varying length, often uttered when the bird may be very high in the sky. In Scotland, this call gives the bird its local name of rain-goose, with the call signifying the coming of rain – which is not that unlikely in Scotland!

On the breeding lochs, birds indulge in ritual displays especially at and with intruding birds. Initially the pair swim purposely towards new arrivals, their heads and bills pointing upwards and forwards, and as they get close they start bill dipping and splash diving. As excitement grows, the territorial pair initiates the snake dance in which they swim slowly side by side with the rear of their bodies submerged and their front halves raised with bent neck and open lowered bill, calling in a duet of moaning calls. Finally they change to the intense but silent 'plesiosaur-race'. With near vertical bodies and bills pointing high into the sky they race back and forth across the water; often the intruders join in. In contrast, the true courtship of the pair is subdued and involves bill dipping and lying flat on the water as well as splash diving before going ashore to mate. It is thought that pairs stay together from year to year and that the pair bond is loosely maintained in the winter.

The nest is just a scrape on the ground or on vegetation or moss very close to the water's edge. It is often made of a heap of aquatic vegetation or moss collected by the birds and further nest building is undertaken when water levels rise. As with other divers, their nests are liable to be lost from flooding and occasionally stranded due to drought, although birds will drag themselves up to 20 metres to get to a stranded nest. Sites are often re-used from year to year. Some nests are hidden in fringing vegetation on lochs and tundra pools but other nests may be out in the open. Eggs are laid from early May to mid-July,

*An incubating bird hiding from predators.*

due to latitude and their ability to lay one or two repeat clutches if eggs are lost. The normal clutch is two, although about a fifth or less may have only one egg; three eggs are exceptional. The eggs are similar to other divers but smaller and darker.

Both parents incubate from the first egg with the female doing the larger share. Birds are very quiet on the nest and lie neck-down in a hiding posture when danger approaches. At other times they sit normally and occasionally re-arrange

33

nest vegetation or stab at flies. When threatened the bird slips off the nest and dives away from the nesting area. Eggs hatch at a month and young leave the nest at a day old. They stay in close proximity to the nesting area and food is brought to them by one adult while the other guards them. The first down plumage is dark brown though paler underneath. This changes to dark grey after a week or so and is replaced by the grey and white juvenile plumage from one month of age. As they grow, both parents travel to the sea or larger lakes to catch fish which they ferry back in their bills. Unattended young often lurk in the bankside vegetation and the nesting water may appear deserted until a parent returns with a feed. Young can at times scramble short distances overland to a larger loch but normally they remain at their home base until they can fly at about seven weeks when they become independent.

Autumn migration starts from July for failed breeders and continues well into September for late-hatched juveniles. As the midnight sun sinks and dims in northern lands Red-throated Divers gather on larger lakes and coastal waters to indulge in group activities; yet most birds migrate in pairs or small parties. They travel overland with ease and can make long crossings of land or oceans to reach their winter quarters. At prominent coastal headlands, a light but continuous passage of divers takes place and large totals of passing birds may be recorded. In autumn and winter quarters they can occur in large concentrations but tend to feed in a dispersed fashion, joining up when resting or to roost at night. In estuaries they often fly in at dawn to feed and return to deeper water before dusk. The summer plumage and the flight feathers are moulted in the late fall and the adults are flightless for nearly a month. A new breeding plumage, involving only a moult of the body feathers, is grown in late winter after which the Red-throated Divers are ready to move north to reclaim their distant arctic breeding grounds.

*A pair of Red-throated Divers at their nesting site
in a small sedgy island on a Swedish lake.*

Red-throated Divers often fly to larger lakes or the sea to
bring back small fish for their young.

# Black-Throated Diver

Black-throated Divers are midway in size between Great Northern and Red-throated Divers. The black pointed bill is less heavy than that of the Great Northern Diver and the forehead is sloping rather than stepped. The bill is straight and never carried up-tilted like the Red-throated Diver. In summer the plumage is a beautiful mixture of black, grey and white; the neck is patterned with black and white stripes while the glossy black back is marked by four patches of white blotches. The back of the neck and head is pale grey with a glossy black throat and the underparts are white. The eye is red and the legs and feet grey-black. Siberian birds are slightly larger and the black throat is glossed green. In winter, Black-throated Divers are dark brown above with white underparts and on the water this species shows a distinctive white flank patch at the water line.

Black-throated Divers live in a similar fashion to other divers, but the flight is a little slower than Red-throated Divers and the wings are not raised as high on the upstroke. They fly long distances on migration and spend the winter on the sea where they tend to be more solitary and do not live in large winter flocks. On the breeding grounds they will fly to other waters to feed, but mostly stay on the breeding lakes, which are larger and more productive than the usual nesting sites of Red-throated Divers.

The principal food is fish which is caught underwater. Birds may remain submerged for up to two minutes, although dives usually last less than a minute. Divers can travel several hundred metres under water. In winter, marine shoaling fish such as small cod and gobies are favourite prey in European waters and birds may at times hunt together in small groups. On the breeding grounds, Black-throated Divers catch a wide selection of freshwater species, such as trout, char and minnows, but will also eat invertebrates such as dragonflies and beetles.

About 150 pairs of Black-throated Divers breed in the Scottish Highlands, principally in Sutherland, Wester Ross and the Western Isles, with lesser numbers elsewhere in the Highland Region, northern Perthshire and Argyll. Occasional pairs have nested southwards to Dumfries and Galloway but the species has shown a decline in this century. Only small numbers winter off the Scottish coast but up to 1,000 may winter along the southern coasts of the British Isles, but these will include Scandinavian birds.

The main breeding grounds of this species are in Norway, Sweden, Finland and Russia. In Scandinavia they breed throughout the forested regions as well as in the tundra regions of the north. In some areas they are quite numerous, and an estimate of 2,000 pairs has been given for Finland. Small numbers occur in the Baltic States but they are common throughout the boreal forest and tundra areas of Russia south to 55 degrees north as well as northwards to the larger islands of the Arctic Ocean. In the east they breed south to northern Kazakhstan and the mountains of northern Mongolia. East of Lake Baikal, the nominate race is replaced by the eastern Siberian Black-throated Diver (*viridigularis*) which is slightly larger and has the black throat glossed dark green. It breeds in similar habitats eastwards to the Pacific coast of Siberia, with small numbers breeding in north-west Alaska where it meets the Pacific Diver.

In winter, Black-throated Divers are found in coastal waters from southern Sweden and Norway along the European coast to France and northern Spain, including the British Isles. These birds are breeders from Europe as well as the northern parts of Russia, where the tundra nesting population moves north to the Arctic Ocean before turning west towards Europe. Boreal forest nesting birds of Russia and Siberia move overland to winter on large inland seas such as the Black and Caspian Seas as well as the northern Mediterranean, while the eastern Siberian breeders move south-east to winter along the coasts of Japan and China.

In Scotland, we expect to see the first Black throated Divers back on their breeding

*In the Scottish Highlands, Black-throated Divers usually breed on larger lochs with wooded islands where they make their nest close to the water's edge.*

*A pair of Black throated Divers swimming across a Scandinavian lake.*

lochs in late March with the majority arriving in early April. The weather can often be bleak with snow showers and gales but the first wailing of the divers is a real sign of spring. In the Arctic, breeding birds have to wait for the ice to thaw and nesting lochs may not be reclaimed until late May or even June. Black-throated Divers breed on lochs usually larger than 25 hectares. On large lochs, holding several pairs or more, the divers require 50–150 hectares per pair. In tundra areas, birds will sometimes nest on smaller lakes and will travel to nearby waters, and even the sea, to catch fish in a rather similar manner to Red-throated Divers.

Black-throated Divers defend their territories which are used from year to year. They usually arrive as pairs on the nesting lochs and quickly start courtship. The display of this species is midway between those of the Red-throated and Great Northern Diver. The male is very vocal, uttering wails and long croaking calls to neighbouring pairs and flying birds. The pair will chase off other Black-throated Divers. During these performances, the birds hold their necks in an S-shaped posture and engage in circular dances. If intruders do not leave, the resident pair engage in bill dipping, rushing and splash diving as well as frequent calling. They will occasionally fight and on very rare occasions serious injury or even death will occur. Courtship between the pair is more subdued with bill dipping, splash diving and underwater rushes. After displaying the female swims ashore and copulation takes place on land.

Nests are built close to the water's edge, usually on islands on lochs. Males do most of the initial nest building, often in the exact position of previous nests. Materials include water weed, twigs and moss gathered from the nest surrounds as well as from the water. When water levels rise birds may frantically nest build to escape flooding and nests can be over a foot in height. The normal clutch is two eggs, rarely one or three. Eggs are large (average weight 120 grams) and slightly glossy brown with black blotches and spots. The female does most of the incubation which starts with the first egg and lasts for a month.

If eggs are lost the pair will re-lay a second or even third clutch, but only one brood is ever reared.

The young are covered with sooty-brown down at hatching. The first chick may hatch a day or two before the second, and the young spend the first couple of days on the nest platform. Very small fish and invertebrates are caught by one parent and brought to the young which are guarded and brooded by the other parent. Soon they move onto the water, usually in sheltered areas near the nest site. The older chick is often aggressive towards the smaller one and this can lead to the death of the chick, especially if food is scarce. After a few weeks, the second coat of down appears and is paler brown with whiter underparts. This is moulted into the juvenile plumage which is white below and dark brown above, each feather having a pale edge which gives the young birds a scaly appearance at close quarters. The young birds catch their own fish at about two months of age, at which time they are also able to fly. Breeding success is widely variable depending on predation, flooding and food supplies with an average of one chick reared per four pairs in Scotland to double this in Sweden.

By late July failed breeders are starting to congregate in small groups prior to leaving the breeding lochs and in August and early September the family parties also leave. In Scotland the birds move to favourite coastal bays in August where they gather into small flocks prior to migration. Throughout their range Black-throated Divers move to the coast in autumn or travel overland south to large inland seas. They are competent travellers on migration, with some birds reaching the Baltic Sea after a 6,000 kilometre flight from Siberia. Once on the sea, adult birds start an autumn moult which gives them a plumage rather similar to the brown and white juveniles; later, after midwinter, they moult their wing feathers and become flightless, at the same time gaining their new nuptial plumage.

# Pacific Diver

The Pacific Diver or Loon breeds in the tundra zone and northern boreal forests of Alaska and Canada. Previously this bird was called the Arctic Loon or Black-throated Diver but in the last decade the American Ornithologists Union have recognised it as a distinct species in line with the earlier views of Soviet ornithologists. Nevertheless much of its lifestyle is very similar to the Black-throated Diver of Europe and Russia. The plumage is very similar to the Black-throated Diver but in summer the black throat has a distinctive purple gloss while the nape and hind neck are very pale grey. The bird is also smaller in body size and allegedly more agile. In winter plumage, the Pacific Diver is supposed not to show a distinctive white flank patch as in the Black-throated Diver, while Russian ornithologists consider the Pacific Diver to have black instead of dark brown feathers in front of and behind the eye in summer plumage, as well as a thinner timbre to its calls.

The Pacific Diver nests on medium to large lakes in the arctic and subarctic regions of North America, from southern Baffin Land and Hudson Bay westwards through the North West and Yukon Territories of Canada to Alaska, with the exception of southern Alaska and the Aleutian islands. They also breed in the coastal tundra of eastern Siberia south to Anadyr and west along the north coast to the Indigirka river. In eastern Siberia and north-west Alaska both species breed but the Black-throated Diver tends to breed on more inland lakes whereas the Pacific Diver is nearer to the coast. Detailed study is required in these areas of overlap to understand the relationship of these two closely related species.

Birds arrive on the breeding lakes in May and even early June in Siberia where they are apparently later than the Black-throated Diver. The breeding behaviour is similar to the Black-throated Diver with the nest being built close to the shore line, mainly on islands. The displays are similar, with the female enticing the male ashore for copulation and the birds being territorially aggressive to other divers including the smaller Red-throated Diver. The normal clutch is two eggs; they are similarly coloured but smaller than Black-throated Diver eggs. Breeding success is very dependent on rodent cycles with predation by red and arctic foxes, glaucous gulls and jaegers being serious in years with low numbers of lemmings. In Arctic areas, young may be forced onto rivers and even the sea before they can fly because of ice forming on nesting lakes. Sometimes young fail to fledge and die because of the early onset of winter.

In the north, birds start to leave their nesting grounds in August with most having departed by early September. Migration routes of the North American birds are westwards to Alaska and south through the Bering Straits and thus down the Pacific coast of North America. They winter in large numbers south to Baja California. The Siberian birds travel eastwards to the Bering Straits and move south either along the North American coasts or down the Russian coast to winter off Kamchatka and Japan.

Pacific Divers are common in the deeper coastal waters of California; the first fall migrants arrive there in late September with the main passage from mid-October with a peak in mid-November and tailing off in mid-December. Large numbers migrate through on the same days with a maximum count of 17,000 Pacific Divers passing Point Pinos in Monterey County on 15th November 1958. During the winter, they tend to congregate in flocks outside the kelp line and up to ten miles or more offshore. Spring passage occurs from March to mid-May and a spring count near Monterey Bay gave over a million birds flying north between March and May 1979. Small numbers of immature birds may linger in southern waters throughout their first year of life but the great majority of the population heads north for another summer in the Arctic.

*Divers often swim with their heads underwater looking for fish, before actually diving and pursuing their prey. This Pacific Diver shows off the diagnostic very pale grey top to the head and neck.*

*A family of Pacific Divers at their nest in the North West Territories.*
*One adult offers a small fish to a recently hatched chick, while the other*
*one waits for its turn under the opposite wing of its parent.*
*The adult in territorial behaviour shows the characteristic*
*purple-glossed throat of this species.*

# White-Billed Diver

This is the largest diver of all but it is also the one most difficult to see. In summer it breeds in far-off frozen lands while in winter it frequents the inhospitable coasts of the northern Pacific Ocean and northern Norway. The White-billed Diver is most closely related to the Great Northern Diver and is similar in general appearance. The most striking difference is the large bill which is pale yellow and upturned; in fact at times it looks too big and clumsy for the bird! The bill is carried uptilted in the manner of the Red-throated Diver but made more pronounced by a bump on the forehead. At close range, the black plumage of the head and neck is glossed purple rather than green; the white streaks of the necklace and half collars are fewer and broader while the white blotches on the mantle are larger and more showy. In summer this is a most beautiful bird and I'll never forget the adult in full summer plumage which frequented the coast near my home in Scotland some years ago.

In winter, it is more difficult to identify White-billed Divers because of confusion with pale Great Northern Divers. The bill is still distinctive but some White-billed Divers have dull bills while some Great Northern Divers have pale bills, but the shape and the carriage of the bill is distinctive. The brown upperparts are generally less contrasting with the white underparts than in the Great Northern Diver and they are often scaly rather than spotted. The face and the sides of the head are pale especially around the eye. Like Great Northern Divers they are expert under water, easily staying submerged for a minute or more to catch a variety of fish; they are more often found in marine inlets, bays and fjords than the open sea.

White-billed Divers breed on the tundra lakes of the high Arctic. In North

America they breed from the north-west coastal plains of Hudson Bay, westwards through the North West Territories to the northern parts of Alaska, with small numbers breeding southwards to the Seward Peninsula. In Russia, they occur from the coasts of the Bering Straits to the southern part of Novaya Zemlya, with sporadic breeding west to Murmansk. Often breeding pairs are scattered in low numbers but higher breeding densities occur in the Taimyr and Chukot peninsulas.

In spring, White-billed Divers migrate along the Arctic coasts of North America and Russia to gather on open leads of water in the Arctic Ocean where they wait for the spring thaw to open the inland lakes. Some are thought to travel overland from the Pacific coast to the Great Slave Lake. Birds start to move inland to their nesting sites in early June, but usually have to wait until mid-June and in cold summers even into the first days of July. The breeding lakes can be as small as low-rimmed tundra pools of only 17 hectares to larger freshwaters and rivers in the tree-less tundra from sea level to the mountains. Nests are similar to those of Great Northern Divers, being close to the water's edge and often just a scrape in the ground lined with grasses and cottongrass. This species is less dependent on the safety of islands for nesting than other divers.

White-billed Divers are thought to maintain life-long pair bonds and often pairs arrive together at the nesting sites; displays and behaviour are very similar to the Great Northern Diver although the calls are louder and harsher. This species calls in flight with a cackling tremulo sound which can be heard echoing across the tundra. Copulation takes place on the shore line as soon as the birds arrive, because of the urgency to complete the breeding cycle during the short summer. Two eggs are usually laid from mid-June; they are typical diver eggs being olive to umber-brown, spotted and blotched black. They are large eggs and

*These two birds were found sick on the coast of northern Scotland in June and were cared for in captivity; they clearly show the differences between the Great Northern Diver (on left) and White-billed Diver in summer plumage.*

weigh up to 160 grams, reflecting the large size of the White-billed Diver. Both sexes incubate, usually facing the water when sitting; they are very alert and leave the nest quickly if disturbed. As with other species in the Arctic, eggs and small young are subjected to high predation in years of low lemming numbers, when predators such as foxes, wolves, gulls and jaegars are desperate for food.

The young hatch at several day intervals so one is larger than the other at the start and this can lead to the death of the smaller chick. The young are cared for by one adult and often brooded on the shore while the other adult catches fish or flies to other lakes or the sea to hunt and return with food. Feeding is mostly done in the early morning and the evening with the young often hiding in fringing vegetation along the shore of the lake. From an early age the young spend time diving which helps them escape from aerial predators. Their parents protect them and are also aggressive to Black-throated and Pacific Divers. There is relatively little published information on breeding success or family life but adults start to leave the breeding lakes in August with young moving to other lakes and rivers in late August and September, as the inland lakes start to freeze.

By the end of September, all the White-billed Divers have moved to the coasts where they moult into winter plumage. As winter approaches small parties travel along the Arctic coasts to pass through the Bering Straits. North American breeders travel south to the coasts of southern Alaska and British Columbia, while the Russian birds winter in the Bering Sea as far south as northern Japan. The birds which breed in the western half of Siberia move west to winter along the north Norwegian coast. Stragglers occur farther south on the Pacific coasts and in western Europe, with even a few in breeding plumage being observed in spring far to the south of their usual haunts.

# Diver Problems

Divers are primitive birds which have wandered the byways of the northern hemisphere for millions of years. They have survived the earth's climatic upheavals as well as the daily competition between hunter and hunted, yet in the last century they have had to endure more problems than ever before. For them it is now a struggle and at times their future looks bleak, yet at the same time there is hope. Now at least their plight is understood and they are loved as very special birds – the very spirit of the northern forests and the Arctic tundra.

Divers are very specialised hunters; superbly equipped to pursue and catch fish underwater using their big webbed feet set well back on their bodies, they are at a disadvantage on land and can only shuffle short distances. In consequence, the nest must be built close to the water's edge and this can result in nest failures due to rising or falling water levels, as well as the eggs being vulnerable to predators. Of course this is a natural part of the rich fabric of life, and creatures from red fox and otter to arctic fox and polar wolf have always searched for diver eggs, while great skuas and glaucous gulls have snatched chicks from their parents. But adult divers are long-lived birds and breeding failures in one or two years can be made up in the following season.

Divers are also affected by variations in the weather, especially in the high Arctic when cold late springs can prevent them nesting in time to allow the full breeding cycle to be completed before the return of winter. Diseases identified as killing divers include normal avian diseases like aspergillosis and botulism, the latter being particularly prevalent in some years on Lake Michigan where over 3,000 Great Northern Divers were found dead in both 1963 and 1964. Divers can also be weakened by internal parasites and about 40 species of internal parasites have been identified in Great Northern Divers. In the winter of 1983, about 7,500 Great Northern Divers were found dead along the Gulf coast of Florida and more have been found in more recent winters. These divers are emaciated and heavily infested with a trematode parasite which is found in the blue crab; the divers were eating the crabs, but there is still debate about whether the real cause of death was the parasites or the fact that the divers were unhealthy due to mercury poisoning on the breeding grounds.

For several thousand years, man has also been a hunter of divers for food as well as feathers and bones for adornment. Relatively low level hunting using ancient techniques may have led to localised pressure on populations but in the last couple of hundred years the balance has been tipped as our ability to kill animals, to change habitats and to interfere with healthy ecosystems has rapidly increased.

Great Northern Divers were regarded as good sport by people with guns in the last century and the first half of this century, and many were killed especially in the eastern United States. In some parts of the world, divers are still hunted for food, both eggs and birds, and some populations may no longer be able to sustain this harvest when superior weapons and equipment make hunting ultra-efficient. In the past, birds and eggs were also taken as museum specimens, and in Britain some misguided people still take the eggs of Black-throated and Red-throated Divers nesting in Scotland for their illegal collections of egg shells, despite the possibility of fines of up to £2000 per egg!

Fishermen have often clashed with divers, some believing they are serious competitors; and in the past divers were destroyed to protect fisheries. But there are also other indirect problems including casual disturbance by fishermen causing egg and chick loss, as well as divers being killed by swallowing fish hooks, being entangled in discarded nylon fishing line or by accidentally swallowing lead fishing weights.

Divers can also die in nets and traps set for fish. Inland, on the big lakes of North America, many divers are caught in traps or entangled in gill nets set for fish, with reports of thousands of Pacific and White-billed Divers being killed in this way in the North West Territories of Canada. It is also a real danger in coastal areas where extensive monafilament nets in the sea can entangle and drown divers. Even in the British Isles, with a relatively low number of divers, this problem has been a cause of concern in recent years and at present is not resolved.

Fisherman, have also changed diver habitats by the development of fishing facilities, by changing water levels with dams and spillways and even by changing the wild fish populations in breeding lochs. Using chemicals to 'clean' the lake of non-target species and restocking with game fish, such as trout, can result in the resident divers being

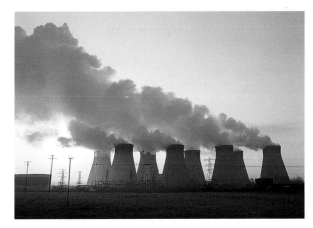

*Toxic gases lead to acid rain.*

denied their preferred selection and size of fish. In recent years, ornithologists were worried about the future of Red-throated Divers in the Shetlands Islands, because Scottish trawlers concentrating on the commercial fishing of sand-eels were thought to be seriously reducing their main food supply.

Recreational water sports can cause serious problems as people use boats to visit, camp and picnic on diver islands causing loss of eggs from chilling or predation. Even the wake from high-speed motor boats can wash out nests, while people in boats can separate young divers from their parents. These pressures can affect diver breeding success but it is also possible for divers on some busy lakes to grow accustomed to people and eventually habituate to the presence of humans by sitting tight instead of leaving their eggs. But do we want all our divers to be tame or should they retain the true spirit of the wild?

Lake-side development is also detrimental to nesting divers; the first few houses or cabins may not affect the birds but ribbon development and over-capacity will in the end lower the wildlife value of even the largest lakes. Nearly always the people involved do not want to harm divers or any other wildlife and in some ways their presence can protect the divers from other dangers. But it is so difficult not to upset the balance. Increases in the number of people living in previously undeveloped areas can lead to more waste food and greater protection from larger predators which can selectively aid an increase in scavengers like foxes and crows, which subsequently eat more diver eggs.

During this century, oil pollution has killed many divers and any tanker accident in northern seas is likely to include divers in the casualty lists. More insidious because they are invisible are the environmental pollutants, such as DDT, dieldrin and PCBs, all of which have been identified in diver tissue and eggs, with studies showing that eggshell thinning has occurred in the Great Northern Diver. No evidence, however, has yet been advanced to show that this has caused declines in diver populations as has occurred with raptors. Most serious is the link between the acidification of lakes through acid rain and the uptake of mercury in the aquatic food chain. Increased levels of mercury have been found in divers and this interferes with the nervous system and leads to behavioural changes and failure to reproduce. Additionally, acidification of lakes also causes reductions in fish stocks to the detriment of divers. All in all divers have had to take some real knocks but they still survive and people are now trying to help them combat the trials of modern life.

# Diver Conservation

The first steps towards a better future for divers were made by those who wrote of nature; they wrote of the wilderness and the spirit of the diver at a time when these birds were just considered exciting sport for the man with a gun. Slowly the tide turned. Divers became protected species and they benefited from campaigns to save wild places.

Protection by statute contains no certainty that divers will survive the ever changing world in which we live. Thirty years ago divers were still being destroyed by some trout fishermen as vermin but this quickly ceased as interest in wildlife conservation increased. Nevertheless divers were encountering new problems as their breeding lochs were affected by hydro-electric dams, afforestation and leisure activities. In the early 1970s, annual monitoring of breeding divers was started in Scotland and it was found that Black-throated Divers, in particular, were rearing very low numbers of young. This was made even worse by the continued loss of eggs to illegal egg-collectors. At the same time, similar concern for Great Northern Divers in the United States showed that they were declining or had even disappeared from some lakes. Just in time, the efforts of Loon researchers and enthusiasts in states from New Hampshire to Minnesota started to expose the story of the Loon's decline.

First of all, came the public concern and the immediate desire to protect divers, their nests and habitats. In Scotland, the RSPB encouraged people to take an interest in breeding divers and to care for them by keeping clear of the nesting islands during incubation. In the States, public awareness programmes encouraged people to care for the future of divers by keeping clear of nests and family parties, especially when in boats. Camp sites were located away from traditional nesting sites and local home-owners adopted their local Loons. In fact, over there a nation fell in love with the Loon.

In North America, thousands of volunteers are now involved in protecting Great Northern Divers, while Loon associations and clubs are active across the country. In June

1992, I spent an exciting day with the Loon Rangers of New Hampshire. Betsy McCoy Poirier of the Loon Preservation Committee told me how the Great Northern Divers of New Hampshire had doubled since the dangerously low numbers of the 1970s. I watched volunteers roping off a bay on Lake Winnipesaukee where a pair of Loons had recently laid eggs. We checked nest sites where pairs would soon be laying eggs and I was impressed how well they were doing despite such high numbers of people, boats and lake-side houses.

Public support is important but unravelling the real problems is also essential. Thankfully, divers have attracted some dedicated scientists in the last 25 years. Judy McIntyre's pioneering work in Minnesota in 1970 has spread to other states and encouraged others to join the search for an understanding of Great Northern Divers. In Scotland, biologists and conservation staff working for the RSPB have followed the fortunes of Black-throated and Red-throated Divers. Now over 20 years later, that knowledge is greatly expanded and many of the problems for divers are being addressed. Some are easier to solve than others.

Early research showed that breeding success was affected by water level fluctuations as well as by disturbance by humans and predation. There was a clear need to increase the numbers of successfully breeding pairs and one way was to use artificial floating islands to overcome changing water levels; they could also be sited away from disturbance. In some areas of the United States, Great Northern Divers readily took to using floating islands and this is now an established management technique in many parts of North America as well as in other countries. It has proved effective in increasing both breeding success and the numbers of pairs. Various types of islands have been built and I was surprised to see Great Northern Divers nesting on such small and simple ones made of logs.

In the Scottish Highlands, initial attempts to encourage Black-throated and Red-throated Divers to use floating islands were made in Argyll in the 1970s but it was not until the late 1980s that a major programme of artificial nesting islands for Black-throated Divers was initiated by the Forestry Commission and the RSPB. Successful use soon followed and now over 40 islands are available to divers in the Highlands. Pairs which had been flooded out year after year are now able to rear young and other lochs, where pairs no longer attempted to breed, have been recolonised.

But islands should not be used on lochs where the birds do not have manifest problems from man's activities; in fact the long-term aim should be to encourage the birds to nest again in natural sites, once the man-made problems have been removed. Wherever possible, wild creatures should be allowed to live as natural a life as possible but some lochs are now so changed that floating islands and wardening will always be required.

*Great Northern Diver nesting raft.*

Sadly, divers still have serious times ahead. Some of these problems will be easier to solve than others. For example, accidental deaths due to fishing line, hooks and lead sinkers can be lessened if fishermen are more careful. Programmes to encourage fishers to recycle discarded monafilament fishing line have been successful and are a considerable contribution to keeping waterways clear of dangerous line, which can entangle wildlife. The use of non-toxic sinkers is also important because the ingestion of lead fishing sinkers by divers is an indiscriminate killer.

Commercial monofilament nets are also lethal to all species of divers in both freshwater and marine localities. There have been disappointingly high numbers of Red-throated Divers killed in nets around the western coasts of the British Isles, but this problem is world-wide and not just confined to divers for the nets kill other birds, mammals and non-target fish. Further research and control is urgently required in view of the high mortality of protected species. In many ways, these nets are an unacceptable method of fishing and should be banned.

Finally, the most serious issue for the long-term well-being of divers is acid rain, whereby toxic exhaust gases from power plants, industries and automobiles are deposited by rain and snow into the lakes and rivers. It is particularly significant in regions where the underlying rocks increase the aquatic environment's susceptibility to acid rain. Increasing levels of acidity in the lakes cause planktons to die and the ecosystem to change drastically; the lakes become clearer and in the end fish die as well – and a lake with no fish is no use to divers.

New research by the RSPB in the Highlands is looking into the reasons why Black-throated Diver chicks fail to survive on some lochs. It has been suggested that there is a shortage of suitably sized fish for the young and that the lochs are no longer so productive. Some of these changes may be due to increased pollution but there is also a view that long term over-grazing by sheep and red deer has led to a decrease in biological productivity of the whole ecosystem.

The changes in acidity also cause toxic chemicals, such as mercury, to become more active in the system and through the food chain it accumulates in top predators like divers. Some die and many more are incapacitated; unable to dive or feed or breed or survive, their nervous systems are stressed by mercury. These problems have been most acute in North America but may be occurring in Europe.

The answer is simple, the action more difficult. We have to reduce the emissions but at present there's still too much talk and not enough action. If the plight of these beautiful birds can help in that campaign, it will benefit not only divers but the future of the earth.

# WORLD DISTRIBUTION OF DIVERS

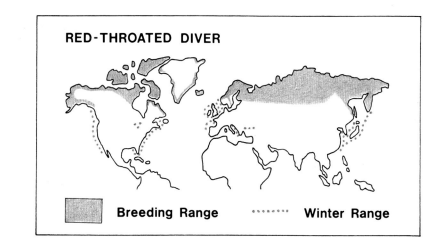

**RED-THROATED DIVER**

Breeding Range     •••••• Winter Range

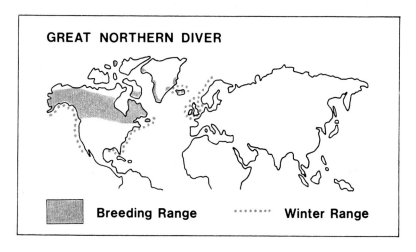

**GREAT NORTHERN DIVER**

Breeding Range     •••••• Winter Range

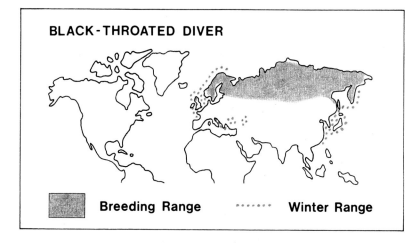

**BLACK-THROATED DIVER**

Breeding Range     •••••• Winter Range

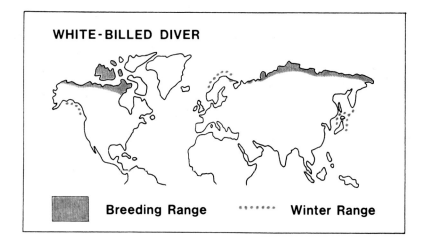

**WHITE-BILLED DIVER**

Breeding Range     •••••• Winter Range

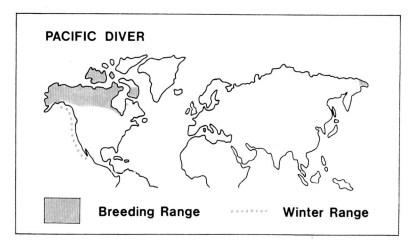

**PACIFIC DIVER**

Breeding Range     •••••• Winter Range

# Enjoying Divers

For the British bird-watcher, Scotland is an excellent country for seeing divers. In summer, Black-throated Divers can be found on the larger lochs throughout the Highlands and the Western Isles. Nesting pairs are often found on lochs beside public roads and it's possible to sit by the car and view them without disturbance. Do not approach the nest site, as they can be shy and leave their nests thus exposing the eggs to predators. It is illegal to intentionally disturb divers at their nests. The best months to watch them are May to July, and to hear them calling to best advantage you cannot beat dawn or dusk.

Red-throated Divers are most easily seen in Shetland, Orkney and the Western Isles but are also found in good numbers through the peaty moorlands of the mainland as far south as Perthshire. They are more difficult to watch when nesting and need to be viewed from a distance of half a mile or more. They do visit larger lochs to fish or gather in groups and this is a good time to study them. They regularly fly overland, so listen out for their rain-goose calls 'ga-ga-ga-gag'.

In autumn, both species move to coastal waters, with Black-throats favouring the larger bays of the west coast of the Highlands where up to 30 birds may be seen prior to migration. Red-throats gather in even larger groups along the Moray Firth and Aberdeenshire coasts. In winter, the latter are common along the east coast, and one of the best places to see them flighting in at dawn and out at dusk is Chanonry Ness on the Black Isle.

Great Northern Divers are regular visitors in coastal waters between October and April, especially on the west and north coasts. Bays and sheltered waters in Shetland, Orkney, Sutherland, Wester Ross, Skye and Argyll may hold groups of 6–20 individuals or more. In April, even larger flocks may occur in places like Loch Eriboll and Loch Broom and the large bays of Orkney and Shetland. This is the best time to see them as they are in their immaculate summer plumage. Breeding records are very exceptional but single adults or more often immatures occur throughout the summer months. White-billed Divers occur as vagrants at any month of the year, probably more often in Shetland than elsewhere. To see a Pacific Diver one needs to visit the northern and western parts of North America.

# Diver Facts

| | Great Northern Diver | White-billed Diver | Black-throated Diver | Pacific Diver | Red-throated Diver |
|---|---|---|---|---|---|
| Scientific | *Gavia immer* | *Gavia adamsii* | *Gavia arctica* | *Gavia pacifica* | *Gavia stellata* |
| American | Common Loon | Yellow-billed Loon | Arctic Loon | Pacific Loon | Red-throated Loon |
| French | Plongeon imbrin | Plongeon à bec blanc | Plongeon arctique | – | Plongeon catmarin |
| German | Eistaucher | Gelbschnäbel-Eistaucher | Prachttaucher | – | Sterntaucher |
| Swedish | Islom | Vitnäbbad Islom | Storlom | – | Smålom |

**Average measurements:**

| | Great Northern Diver | White-billed Diver | Black-throated Diver | Pacific Diver | Red-throated Diver |
|---|---|---|---|---|---|
| Length (cms) | 69–91 | 76–91 | 58–73 | 57–70 | 53–69 |
| Wingspan (cms) | 127–147 | 137–155 | 110–130 | 110–120 | 106–116 |
| Tail (cms) | 58–75 | 62–72 | 51–67 | | 47–57 |
| Bill length (cms) | 72–89 | 83–96 | 52–68 | 48–66 | 46–61 |
| Weight (gms) | 2,270–4,480 | 4,000–6,400 | 1,300–3,400 | | 1,100–1,800 |
| Normal clutch | 2 | 2 | 2 | 2 | 2 |
| Egg size (mm) | 90 × 58 | 89 × 57 | 84 × 52 | 75 × 47 | 75 × 48 |
| Egg weight (gms) | 167 | 160 | 120 | | 83 |
| Incubation period | 24–25 days | | 28–30 days | | 26–28 days |

## Recommended Reading

*The Common Loon – Spirit of the Northern Lakes* by Judith McIntyre published in 1988 by the University of Minnesota Press is the acknowledged monograph for this species; it is a splendid read, full of fascinating information and thoroughly recommended for anyone interested in Loons. There are a variety of other publications about Loons for the avid reader including *The Loon* by Joan Dunning, Yankee Books, 1985; *Loon Magic* by Tom Klein, Northword Press, 1985; and *Love of Loons* by Mike Link and Kate Crowley, Voyageur Press, 1987.

## Biographical Note

Roy Dennis is a professional ornithologist living near Loch Garten in the Scottish Highlands. For 8 years in the 1960s, he and his wife ran the Bird Observatory on Fair Isle, famous for bird migration and seabirds. From 1971 to 1991, he was the Royal Society for the Protection of Birds' senior officer in the Scottish Highlands and his varied duties included close involvement in the protection and conservation of Black-throated and Red-throated Divers. He is now a self-employed wildlife consultant; a specialist on birds of prey and a well-known lecturer, broadcaster and writer.